CW00541811

THIS BOOK BELONGS TO

....

Zizi loves playing in the garden,
All day in the dirt and mud.

His mummy shouts
"Dinner's ready!"
Off his wellies come with a thud.

"Wash your hands" his mummy says,
"You know what you need to do."

Off Zizi goes to clean his hands,
To wash away the germs and flu.

Zizi learnt about all the germs,
And maybe we should too.

So here's a story for us to learn,
What is false and what is true.

Germs are good and bad,
Bacteria makes us strong,
But some germs are very mean,
So let's learn what's right and wrong.

Vinny the virus is a
very naughty germ,
He'll make you too sick to
leave your bed.

So lets wash our hands,
SCRUB! SCRUB! SCRUB!
By doing this he
cannot spread!

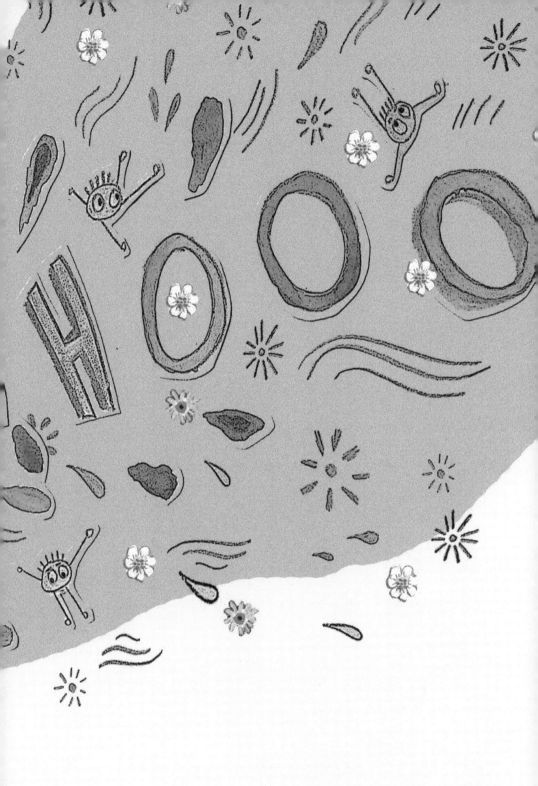

Barry the bad bacteria
can make you feel glum,
So make sure you eat all
of your fruits and greens.

So if Barry turns up,
make sure you shout,
"I am BIG, I am STRONG...
stop being mean!"

Here comes Gina the good bacteria...
She's always here, helping you and me.
Making sure we stay safe and strong,
Looking after everybody we can see.

Gina needs our help,
Let's do this together!
Run around the garden,
Stay healthy and live **FOREVER!**

Let's go back to Zizi's house,
He should have finished his dinner.

The first one to finish their greens,
Is the number one WINNER!

Bath time for Zizi,

SPLISH! SPLASH! SPLOSH!
Then he dries off,
He's had a good wash.

Now let's get in bed,
All warm and cosy,
In our jim-jams,
Starting to feel dozy...

Goodnight Zizi, goodnight friend,
It's time this story comes to an end.

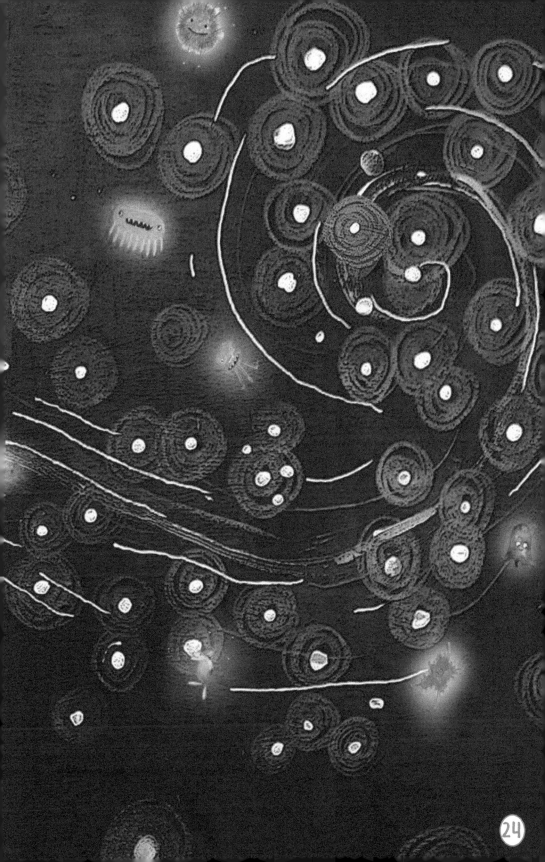

The

End

Dedicated to my loving nephew,
Zion AKA Zizi

Lightning Source UK Ltd.
Milton Keynes UK
UKHW050235230921
390902UK00001BA/7

9 781913 454531